The Snake's Pyjamas

poems selected by
Pie Corbett and Valerie Bloom

Six Things Found in an Elf's Backpack

A bee's sting for giving bullies a sudden shock.
A tooth, that looks like a fresh-water pearl,
  stolen from under a child's pillow.
A floppy hat made from a purple Foxglove.
An old grey hair snatched from a goat's beard,
  to be used for tickling a teacher's nose.
A well-thumbed encyclopaedia of trickery.
A bag of never-ending wishes.

Pie Corbett

Ten Things Found in a Wizard's Pocket

A dark night.
Some words that nobody could ever spell.
A glass of water full to the top.
A large elephant.
A vest made from spiders' webs.
A handkerchief the size of a car park.
A bill from the wand shop.
A bucket full of stars and planets,
  to mix with the dark night.
  A bag of magic mints you can suck for ever.
    A snoring rabbit.

Ian McMillan

A Hot Day

Cotton-wool clouds loiter.
A lawn mower very far
Birrs. Then a bee comes
To a crimson rose and softly,
Deftly and fatly crams
A velvet body in.

A.S.J. Tessimond

The Caterpillar

Brown and furry
Caterpillar in a hurry,
Take your walk
To the shady leaf, or stalk,
    Or what not,
Which may be the chosen spot.
    No toad spy you,
Hovering bird of prey pass by you;
Spin and die,
To live again as butterfly.

Christina Rossetti

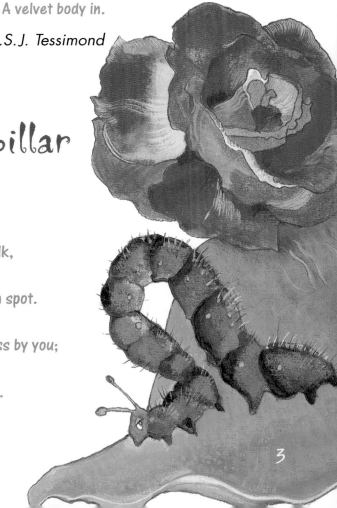

3

The Cabbage White Butterfly

I look like a flower you could pick. My delicate wings
Flutter over the cabbages. I don't make
Any noise ever. I'm among silent things.
      Also I easily break.

I have seen the nets in your hands. At first I thought
A cloud had come down but then I noticed you
With your large pink hand and arm. I was nearly caught
      But fortunately I flew

Away in time, hid while you searched, then took
To the sky, was out of your reach. Like a nameless flower
I tried to appear. Can't you be happy to look?
      Must you possess with your power?

Elizabeth Jennings

Millions of Strawberries

Marcia and I went over the curve,
  Eating our way down
   Jewels of strawberries we didn't deserve,
   Eating our way down,
Till our hands were sticky, and our lips painted.
And over us the hot day fainted,
And we saw snakes,
And got scratched,
And a lust overcame us for the red unmatched
Small buds of berries,
Till we lay down –
Eating our way down –
And rolled in the berries like two little dogs,
Rolled
In the late gold.
  And gnats hummed,
   And it was cold,
    And home we went, home without a berry,
     Painted red and brown,
      Eating our way down.

Genevieve Taggard

Blowing bubbles

Bubbles are beautiful

Bubbles are fun

Bubbles are rainbows

caught in the sun

up float Bubbles

Bubbles float down

Bubbles float sideways

round and round and round

Blow till you're breathless
then when you've done

and

BURST

THEM

j u m P u P

ONE

by

ONE

Patricia Leighton

Listen

Hear the splatter
of the rain
Beat a rhythm
on the pane

Sending ripples through the puddles
Water rushing like a stream
Hear the anger of the rivers
With a scream
Gushing torrents
As the motions of the oceans
Tremble, raging through the seas. 7

Maggie Holmes

Dive and Dip

Rise and rip, dive and dip, leaning backwards with the strain.

Rattling, roaring, upward soaring, swirling, whirling in your brain.

Looping, lunging, downward plunging, going round a dizzy bend.

Swinging, clinging, heads are ringing, holding tightly to a friend.

Hands that clasp, scream and gasp, funny feelings here inside.

Ears are popping now we're stopping.

That's a roller coaster ride.

Max Fatchen

9

Louder!

OK, Andrew, nice and clearly – off you go.

Welcome everybody to our school concert...

Louder, please, Andrew. Mums and dads
won't hear you at the back, will they?

Welcome everybody to our school concert...

Louder, Andrew. You're not trying.
Pro – ject – your – voice.
Take a b i g b r e a t h and louder!

Welcome everybody to our school concert...

For goodness sake, Andrew.
LOUDER! LOUDER!

Welcome every body to our school concert!

Now, Andrew, there's no need to be silly.

Roger Stevens

Surrounded by Noise!

I'm surrounded by noise,
LISTEN!

BEEP! BEEP! BEEP!
A car down on the street.
BOOGIE! BOOGIE! BOOGIE!
A disco beat.

THUMP! THUMP! THUMP!
A hammer next door.
THUD! THUD! THUD!
Brother jumping on the floor.

CLACKETY! CLACKETY! CLACKETY!
A train rattles by.
ROAR! ROAR! ROAR!
A plane climbs the sky.

DRILL! DRILL! DRILL!
A workman on the road.
NO! NO! NO!
Mum about to explode.

We're surrounded by noise,
Just...STOP!
Just...LISTEN!

Ian Souter

Weather

Dot a dot dot dot a dot dot
Spotting the windowpane.
Spack a spack speck flick a flack fleck
Freckling the windowpane.

A spatter a scatter a wet cat a clatter
A splatter a rumble outside.
Umbrella umbrella umbrella umbrella
Bumbershoot barrel of rain.

Slosh a galosh slosh a galosh
Slither and slather a glide
A puddle a jump a puddle a jump
A puddle a pump aluddle a dump a
Puddmuddle jump in and slide!

Eve Merriam

12

Sea Timeless Song

Hurricane come
and hurricane go
but sea...sea timeless
sea timeless
sea timeless
sea timeless
sea timeless

Hibiscus bloom
then dry-wither so
but sea...sea timeless
sea timeless
sea timeless
sea timeless
sea timeless

Tourist come
and tourist go
but sea...sea timeless
sea timeless
sea timeless
sea timeless
sea timeless

Grace Nichols

13

The Cheer-up Song

No one likes a boaster
And I'm not one to boast,
But everyone who knows me knows
That I'm the most.

I'm the most attractive, I'm
The Media Superstar,
One hundred per cent in-tell-i-gent
And pop-u-lar.

All my jokes are funny.
Every one's a laugh.
Madonna pays me money for
My au-to-graph.

For I'm the snake's pyjamas, I'm
The bumble-bee's patella,
I'm a juicesome peach at a picnic on the beach, I'm
The rainmaker's umbrella.

Yes I'm the death-by-chocolate, I'm
The curried beans on toast,
And everyone who knows me knows that
I'm the most.

Tee-rr-eye-double-eff-eye-see
Triffic! TRIFFIC! TRIFFIC!
Yes it's me! ME! MEEE!

14   *John Whitworth*

A Crispy Tale

Millicent Melanie Miriam Mee
ate nothing but crisps
for breakfast and tea.
When her mother asked
what she'd like for lunch,
Millicent Melanie just muttered, 'Crunch!'
It was crisps for each supper
and crisps for her snacks...
she guzzled each day 97 large packs!
The doctor tried warning her
she would be ill,
but Millicent carried on eating her fill...
Salted with vinegar,
beef, barbecue,
every flavour you've heard of –
and some others, too!
You'd think she'd grow fat,
but she shrank to a wisp...
and one day poor Milly turned into a CRISP!

Judith Nicholls

How Can I?

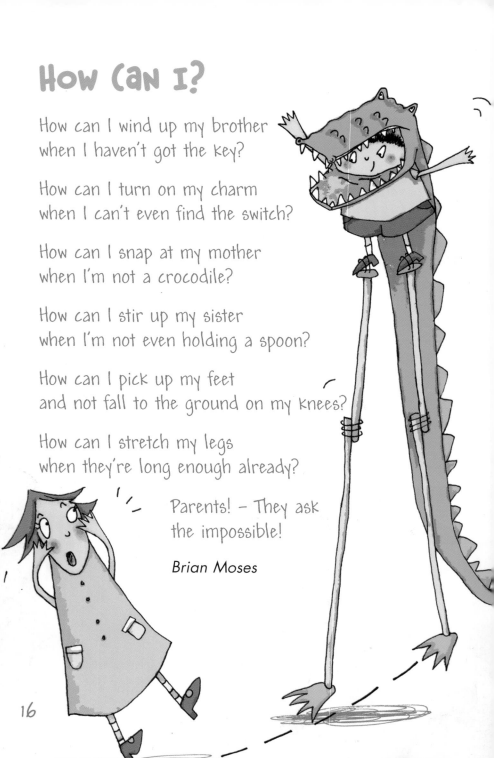

How can I wind up my brother
when I haven't got the key?

How can I turn on my charm
when I can't even find the switch?

How can I snap at my mother
when I'm not a crocodile?

How can I stir up my sister
when I'm not even holding a spoon?

How can I pick up my feet
and not fall to the ground on my knees?

How can I stretch my legs
when they're long enough already?

Parents! – They ask
the impossible!

Brian Moses

Animal riddle

Like a small Bear

                bundles over the dark road,

brushes pAst the front gate,

           as if she owns the joint.

rolls the Dustbin

             like an expert barrel rider

tucks into yesterday's Garbage,

          crunches worms for titbits.

wakes us from dEep sleep,

          blinks back at torchlight.

our midnight feasteR,

      ghost-friend,

      moon-lit,

      zebra bear.

Pie Corbett

17

Jellyfish Stew

Jellyfish stew,
I'm loony for you,
I dearly adore you,
oh, truly I do,
you're creepy to see,
revolting to chew,
you slide down inside
with a hullabaloo.

You're soggy, you're smelly,
you taste like shampoo,
you bog down my belly
with oodles of goo,
yet I would glue noodles
and prunes to my shoe,
for one oozy spoonful
of jellyfish stew.

Jack Prelutsky

Some Favourite Words

Mugwump, chubby, dunk and whoa,
Swizzle, doom and snoop,
Flummox, lilt and afterglow,
Gruff, bamboozle, whoop
And nincompoop.

Wallow, jungle, lumber, sigh,
Ooze and zodiac,
Innuendo, lullaby,
Ramp and mope and quack
And paddywhack.

Moony, undone, lush and bole,
Inkling, tusk, guffaw,
Waspish, croon and cubby-hole,
Fern, fawn, dumbledore
And many more...

Worm.

Richard Edwards

HOW DID HE ESCAPE?

There was a man
in prison who was
famous for escaping –
left all his captors gaping.

So they built him a room
like a mummy's tomb
in their finest gaol
and left him there to rot –
not a jot of a chance
to escape –
no windows,
and the door held fast
with the largest lock
they had in stock!

All he had inside the room
was a wooden table –
and yet,
according to the fable,
ten minutes later
he was free –

So, tell me, tell me,
Alligator –
how was it done?

He rubbed his hands
till they were sore.

He took the saw
and cut the table
right in half.

Two halves make a whole.

So he climbed through the hole.

Once outside –
he cried
till he was hoarse.

He climbed on the horse

and rode away...

Pie Corbett

Who Says a Poem Always Has to Rhyme?

There was a young man called Frank
Who kept his pocket money in the...*

When he'd saved enough he bought an electric viola
And celebrated with a can of co...**

When he plays the viola the whole house rocks
It makes your shoes dance and it frightens your...***

Frank plays his viola all of the time.
Who says a poem always has to...****

Roger Stevens

*Post Office **-conut cordial ***granny
****have a similar sound at the end of the line
as it had at the end of the line before?

Beelzebub

Here I come
Beelzebub
Over my shoulders
I carry my club
In my hand
A dripping pan
Aren't I
A jolly old man.

A Peanut Sat on the Railway Track

A peanut sat on the railway track,
His heart was all a-flutter.
Along came a train –
Toot-toot! – peanut butter!

See You Later, Alligator

See you later, alligator.
In a while, crocodile.
See you later, hot potato.
If you wish, jelly-fish.
Not too soon, big baboon.
Toodle-oo, kangaroo.
Bye-bye, butterfly.

Order in the Court

Order in the court
The judge is eating beans
His wife is in the bath tub
Shooting submarines.

Anon.

Index of Titles

A Crispy Tale, Judith Nicholls 15

A Hot Day, A.S.J. Tessimond 3

Animal riddle, Pie Corbett 17

Blowing bubbles, Patricia Leighton 6

Dive and Dip, Max Fatchen 8

How Can I? Brian Moses 16

How Did He Escape? Pie Corbett 20

Jellyfish Stew, Jack Prelutsky 18

Listen, Maggie Holmes 7

Louder! Roger Stevens 10

Millions of Strawberries, Genevieve Taggard 5

Playground Rhymes, Anon. 23

Sea Timeless Song, Grace Nichols 13

Six Things Found in an Elf's Backpack, Pie Corbett 2

Some Favourite Words, Richard Edwards 19

Surrounded by Noise! Ian Souter 11

Ten Things Found in a Wizard's Pocket, Ian McMillan 2

The Cabbage White Butterfly, Elizabeth Jennings 4

The Caterpillar, Christina Rossetti 3

The Cheer-up Song, John Whitworth 14

Weather, Eve Merriam 12

Who Says a Poem Always Has to Rhyme? Roger Stevens 22